I am Valuable

Dr. Deshunna Monay Ricks

I Am Valuable

ISBN: 978-1-7357171-0-4

This book is dedicated to all children across the world.
You are here on purpose!

don't ever be afraid to be great!

I AM Valuable

You are so full of greatness so don't ever be afraid to be great!

Deja was born on December 29th to her loving parents. Although her parents were young when they had her, they were excited to take her home to their family. Deja was such a cute baby and everyone who saw her wanted to kiss and hold her. Deja loved to laugh, talk, play, sing, and eat of course. Chicken was her favorite food!

When Deja turned five something very bad
happened to her father—he got arrested and
he went to jail. Deja was sad and scared and she
didn't know what to do. She thought to herself,
"Will I ever see my dad again?"

The next day, Deja, her mom, big brother, and little sister moved in with her maternal grandmother. Deja was happy to see her cousins and aunt but she wanted to be back at home with her dad.

When Deja woke-up the next morning she noticed that her mother was not in bed.

She searched all over the house looking for her,
but she could not find her.

Deja begin to cry, and she felt lost and afraid.

Deja waited all day and night for her mother to return but she did not come back home.

Deja said, "What am I going to be without my parents?"

She thought to herself, "Will I ever be great?"

Deja felt broken inside and unloved.

One summer day, when Deja was at school, a social worker came to her class and she had to go live with strangers in a foster home. Deja was very afraid and did not know what to do. She cried to herself and said, "Why is all of this bad stuff happening to me?"

A few months later, Deja and her siblings moved in with their paternal grandmother. Deja wondered, "Will I be moved again?" She said, "Will bad things happen to me in this home too?" Deja begin to imagine what her life would be like if someone were to love her.

Deja's paternal grandmother was a very strong woman because she took care of 8 children by herself and provided them with love and care.

Although Deja was happy to live with her relatives in kinship care, she longed to live with her parents.

While Deja was in her paternal grandmother's home she learned how to pray.

She loved going to church and learning new things.

Although Deja could not sing very well, she joined the RoseBud choir.

She also joined the usher board and was the best marcher of all the children.

On Deja's 12th birthday, she prayed the following prayer,
"Lord, please let me be somebody! I want to be great!
But I don't know if I can do it without my parents."

That night Deja heard a voice say—

"Deja, I love you! You are valuable!
You are important!
I made you to be great!
You will do great things!
All you have to do is believe!"

The next morning, Deja woke-up with a smile on her face, she looked
in the mirror and shouted —

"I AM special!"
"I AM unique!"
"I AM important!"
"I AM enough!"
"I AM powerful"
"I AM gifted!"
"I AM worthy!"
"I AM beautiful!"
"I AM somebody!"
"I AM valuable!"
"I LOVE ME!"

Deja repeated these messages
to herself every day.

So, Deja wants you to do the same thing!

When you are having a bad day, or when you feel sad and lonely, or when other children say mean things to you and do not to play with you, all you need to do is hug yourself and repeat after me: "

I AM special!" "I AM unique!" "I AM important!" "I AM enough!"

"I AM powerful!" "I AM gifted!" "I AM worthy!" "I AM beautiful!"

"I AM somebody!" "I AM valuable!" "I LOVE ME!"

About the Author

DR. DESHUNNA MONAY RICKS was born and raised in West Fresno, California. She was raised by her parents up until age five. Dr. Ricks was raised in foster care from age 8-18 by her paternal grandmother, Hester Hensley. Although experiencing many trails, tribulations, and adversities she was determined to become successful. Dr. Ricks has a master's in social work and a credential in counseling from California State University Fresno. She has a doctorate in education from Brandman University. Dr. Ricks is a counselor in a public K-12 school district and an adjunct instructor at a Christian University. She is the Owner and CEO of I Have Value, LLC and the Owner and President of I AM Valuable (a nonprofit organization). The mission of *I AM Valuable* is to teach individuals to recognize their true identity through storytelling, self-discovery, and self-reflection. Dr. Ricks recently launched Value Academy for teens so that they can learn how truly valuable they are. Her purpose in life is to breathe life into others in order that they may experience wellness. Dr. Ricks is the parent of Va'Ron Mitchell; a handsome young man who has changed her life for the better. Most importantly, she is a child of the Most High God who has made all things possible for her.

Contact information

For more information about **I Am Valuable,** please visit us on
Facebook: IAMValubaleINC or Instagram: iamvaluableinc

For book readings, public speaking engagements, and
consultation please email *ihavevalue2018@gmail.com*

**Deja wants you to remember just how
valuable you are!**

CPSIA information can be obtained
at www.ICGtesting.com
Printed in the USA
BVHW091314240920
589522BV00001B/1